Visitors to the Boat Museum, Ellesmere Port, have the rare privilege of watching an Armstrong steam pumping engine which works. Built in the early 1870s, it worked until 1957 and then lay derelict until its restoration by volunteers between 1977 and 1979.

HYDRAULIC MACHINES

Adrian Jarvis

Shire Publications Ltd

CONTENTS

British Library Cataloguing in Publication Data available.

Set in 9 point Times roman and printed in Great Britain by C. I. Thomas & Sons (Haverfordwest) Ltd, Press Buildings, Merlins Bridge, Haverfordwest, Dyfed.

ACKNOWLEDGEMENTS

The author wishes to acknowledge the help given to him by friends and colleagues in various parts of Britain, but especially the following for their help with illustrations: The Director and staff, HMS *Belfast*; The Isle of Man Harbour Board and Mr Gardner, the Chief Engineer; Messrs Foxall Palmer Ltd, Liverpool. With the exception of the photograph on page 3, all the photographs are the author's, who wishes to thank his colleague David Flower for his help in selection and in turning amateur negatives into good prints. Line drawings are by Mr D. R. Darton.

COVER: *A machine which empties a coal boat into a ship by simply picking it out of the water and turning it upside down, replacing the boat when the coal has fallen out. Located at South Dock, Goole, Humberside, and still working, it works silently and apparently effortlessly.*

LEFT: *The principle of the hydraulic press. A small force acting on a piston of small area over a long travel will create a large force on a piston of large area over a short travel.*

RIGHT: *Diagram of a hydraulic jack. The lever (E) is pumped to force down the ram B1. This forces fluid from reservoir F2 into F1, via non-return valve C, causing the lifting ram (A1) in cylinder A to rise. As ram B1 is raised by the lever, the suction created introduces fluid from the casing reservoir (hatched area) via non-return valve G. This allows the pumping to be repeated, thereby gradually raising the lifting ram in cylinder A. Seals (D) around the rams prevent fluid leaking out of and air leaking into the system. A relief valve (not shown) is opened to allow fluid from cylinder A to escape into the casing reservoir, lowering ram A1.*

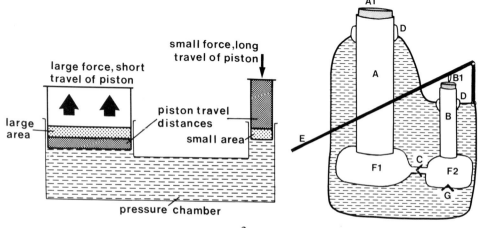

Although London's hydraulic power distribution network has ceased working, hydraulic machines are still being built. The most modern and massive is the Thames Flood Barrier at Woolwich. The ten gates, which span a third of a mile (640 m) are raised and lowered by hydraulic power.

INTRODUCTION

Hydraulic power may be defined as a system for transmitting energy through the medium of water or other incompressible fluid. This definition would, however, include the leat of a watermill, and for the subject of this book we must look to machines which work by the pressure of the medium — *hydrostatic* machines — and mostly exclude those which work by the force of a fluid in motion — *hydrokinetic* machines.

A small hydraulic bottle jack, as used by the do-it-yourself motorist, will serve to introduce the principle. The handle of the jack pushes a small cylindrical plunger, or *ram*, into a cylinder full of fluid. When it enters, it displaces its own volume of the fluid, via a non-return valve, through the delivery passage. The fluid passes into a larger cylinder, in which is a similarly larger ram, and this will be forced upwards by an amount corresponding to the volume of fluid displaced by the small ram. The casing in

which the cylinders are bored also contains a fluid reservoir, so that the cycle may be repeated by raising the handle and pushing it down again until the required displacement of the larger (or lifting) ram has been achieved.

The practical effect is that many strokes of the handle, each requiring little effort, will bring about a much smaller travel of the lifting ram, but that small travel is effected with sufficient force to lift a motor car. It is the fluid pressure which lifts the car: if the lifting ram is made larger it will lift more weight for a given force on the pump handle but will require more strokes to achieve a given amount of lift. If, on the other hand, the pump ram is made larger, fewer strokes will be required, but more force will be required on the handle.

In a bottle jack the fluid normally passes from the pump to the lifting ram through an internal passage in the casing, but the effect would be the same if it passed though an external pipe. If the pipe were not a few inches, but a few yards, or even a few miles, long, because the fluid is incompressible, the work applied at the pump would still be transmitted to the lifting ram, diminished only by the small amount of friction between the fluid and the walls of the pipe.

The hydraulic brakes of virtually all motor vehicles work by just such an arrangement of 'remote hydraulic jacks'. When the motorcyclist squeezes his front brake lever, he forces a small ram into a cylinder full of fluid. This raises the pressure in a system which consists of a pipe down to the front brake and the twin cylinders of the front brake caliper. The twin rams in these cylinders are displaced outwards, causing the brake pads to grip the brake disc, thus slowing down the machine. The braking system of a car is more extensive, but it works in exactly

The rugged simplicity and massive strength of hydraulic machines is seen in this ingot shear, built for steelworks use.

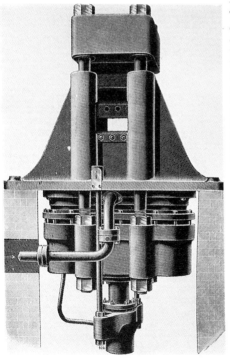

the same manner. Drum brakes work on a different mechanical principle, but the hydraulics are much the same. Whilst the air brakes used on the majority of heavy goods vehicles offer similar advantages, the mechanical brakes used on older motor cars and light commercial vehicles were complicated by comparison and relatively ineffective.

To the nineteenth-century engineer, the possibilities of a system of power transmission which did not require a mechanical connection were very exciting, offering solutions to many problems. From the use of a small handpump or the application of a natural head of water to the employment of a steam pump was a small step. Once it was possible to deliver water at moderately high pressures (700 pounds per square inch, 49.2 kg/sq cm, was a frequent choice) very large forces could be exerted at the delivery end. A modest 6 inch (152 mm) ram would give 8.83 tons and, while the frequency with which this force could be exerted was governed by the power of the engines, the amount of the force itself was not. This power could go anywhere a pipe could go, so that different machines driven on the same system no longer had to stand in any particular position relative to one another or be accurately aligned, as was necessary with mechanical driving. A number of very astute minds were applied to the development of hydraulic machines, and by about 1870 they had established a new technology which served a wide variety of industries. That their achievements are so little known today is remarkable.

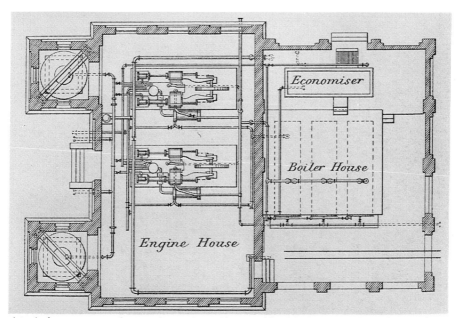

A typical arrangement of a pumping station, with ground level boiler house, elevated engine house and twin accumulators (left), whose towers either side of the door are exploited as an architectural feature. This was built for the Buenos Aires sewage pumping system in 1895.

PIONEERS OF HYDRAULIC POWER

It was the French physicist Blaise Pascal (1623-62) who laid the basis of hydraulic machinery. He propounded what he called 'the equilibrium of liquids' in 1647 and explained the paradox of the multiplication of forces. He demonstrated an apparatus which had a tank of fluid from which rose two open-topped cylinders of different diameters. Each contained a piston and the apparatus could be balanced by placing a large weight on the large piston and a small one on the small piston. If the ratio of the weights was the same as the ratio of the piston areas then the hydrostatic pressure in the system was equalised and a light weight balanced a heavy one.

This was only a piece of laboratory apparatus, and it was a long time before the principle illustrated was applied by a practical man to an industrial purpose. Joseph Bramah (1748-1814) began his working life as a cabinet maker but became an outstanding engineer. The eighteen patents granted to him cover a wide range of contemporary technology, including water closets, fountain pens,

beer engines and the security lock which still bears his name. In 1795 he was granted a patent for the use of water as a medium for transmitting energy. It covered a number of applications, of which the most immediately important was the hydraulic press. This machine worked on the simple 'jack' principle of the multiplication of forces. It solved problems in a number of industries, especially the problem of packing light bulky goods like raw cotton into small dense bales for transport. Until the arrival of Bramah's press, only the screw press was available: it had been little developed since Roman times and a pressure of about 25 tons was its limit. The Bramah press could exert almost any force the customer would pay for, and as early as 1799 a 400 ton press had been built for Joseph Ridgeway. Other industries, notably seed-oil pressing, were to benefit from the hydraulic press, but the most spectacular early installation was in the textile industry. The process known as 'discharging' printed a pattern on to a coloured cloth by partial bleaching under mechanical

In this workshop pit is a hydraulic chain testing machine working on the same principle as Matthew Murray's, and which is still in daily use. Since the demise of the Liverpool Hydraulic Power Company in 1970 this machine has had its own pump.

pressure, and in 1818 a plant was built in Glasgow which contained sixteen presses of 320 tons capacity. Power was supplied by steam pumps and the water pressure was no less than 6.36 tons per square inch (41.6 tonnes/sq cm).

Matthew Murray, a Leeds engineer, developed hydraulic machines for testing and weighing purposes. His best known machine was constructed for the Navy Board for proof-testing ships' anchor cables. 'It will be an immense machine and is intended to exert a pressure of 1000 tons,' wrote Murray, but its construction posed so many problems that others had anticipated some of its features and the 'immense machine' was completed only in 1826, the year of his death. Ironically, the Navy Board bought a similar machine from Bramah's sons, Murray's machine going to another customer.

There is an alternative approach to the use of hand or steam pumps, and that is the harnessing of a natural head of water. If water from a high-level reservoir is led in a pipe to a hydraulic motor at a lower level it will provide free power, and it will not do so from its kinetic energy (as with an undershot waterwheel) but by hydrostatic pressure. Engines working on this principle were built long before

Bramah's press, for pumping out mines: one is recorded in Hungary as early as 1749. They worked like a high-pressure steam engine, with inlet and outlet valves controlling the water, and they were much more efficient than contemporary waterwheels. A whim to improve on the waterwheel brought to prominence William Armstrong, the man who was to turn hydraulic power into a major influence on nineteenth-century industry.

In his patent of 1812, 'Laying water pipes etc', Bramah obtained protection for the idea of using hydraulics not as a prime mover, nor as a 'multiplier of forces', but as a public power distribution service. The only such service then existing was gas supply, and less than a dozen gasworks existed, so Bramah's idea was highly advanced. He did not develop it, however, but the man who did, turning inspiration into reality and profit, was the lawyer who wanted to improve waterwheels, William Armstrong (1810-1900), better known as the arms and engineering magnate Lord Armstrong.

It was Armstrong's good fortune that his first significant hydraulic machine was a quayside crane, for port services represented the greatest potential market for large-scale power transmission systems.

RIGHT: *Natural hydrostatics. If the water in the reservoir is maintained at a constant head it will drive a hydraulic motor. The pressure at the stop valve is expressed in feet head or converted to pounds per square inch by the conversion factor of 0.434.*

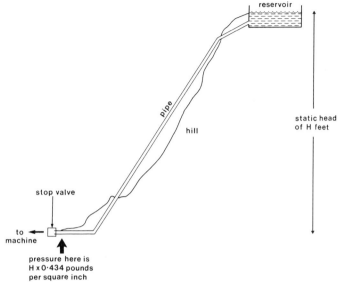

reservoir

pipe

hill

static head
of H feet

stop valve

to ← machine

**pressure here is
H x 0·434 pounds
per square inch**

BELOW, LEFT: *This building is not a folly on a country estate but the valve house at Lake Vyrnwy, North Wales. Its function is to control the level in the lake, which is a water supply reservoir, by hydraulically operated valves.*

BELOW, RIGHT: *Inside the Vyrnwy valve house is this unusual machine. Water from a natural static head enters the large outside cylinders to drive it in exactly the same way that eighteenth-century motors worked. The small rams in the middle provide a small volume of water at sufficient pressure to operate the valves, the cylinders and lifting chains of which can be seen.*

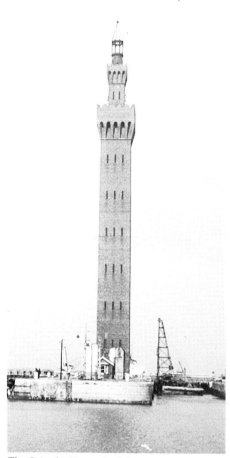

The Grimsby Tower, built by Armstrong about 1849. It stands 300 feet (91.2 m) high and supports a tank of 33,000 gallons (149,820 litres) capacity at a height of 200 feet (60.8 m). It was soon rendered obsolete by the adoption of weight-loaded accumulators, but continued in use until the 1880s.

Not only would the economies of scale of a central power house be appreciated, but the use of small portable steam plants for handling goods represented a fire hazard. The long distances between machines dotted about a dock estate made mechanical transmission impossible, yet the cost of manpower was holding back the expansion of overseas trade. To these problems Armstrong applied

the unfulfilled ideas of others, as well as many of his own.

Initially he thought of hydraulics as a versatile prime mover, exploiting the uncommonly large 200 foot (60.37 m) head of the Newcastle water supply, and when first he supplied machinery in areas where such a head was not available his approach was to create one by pumping water to a high-level reservoir. The magnificent tower built for this purpose at Grimsby must, however, have shown that this was an expensive way of tackling the problem. The alternative was his re-invention of the weight-loaded *accumulator*, a form of which had been employed in the discharging plant in Glasgow. This was a control device for steam pumps which gave the added benefit of a stored reserve of power. Its key benefit, however, was that it facilitated the use of higher pressures, so that for a given amount of power transmitted less water moved through the pipes, making everything less bulky and cutting frictional losses. Armstrong usually employed a pressure of 700 pounds per square inch (49.2 kg/sq cm). The achievement of this pressure by the old method would have required the building of a tower 1615 feet (492.3 m) high. A further benefit of higher operating pressure was that, because less water was used for a given amount of power delivered, less water had to be paid for. Most systems worked on a total loss basis: when the water had done its work in the machine it ran to waste. The alternative was to employ an extensive system of return pipes, but this was so undesirable that it was normally only done where water was either very expensive or very difficult to get rid of because of drainage problems.

Perhaps the most important of Armstrong's other innovations was the *multiplying sheave*. It was easy to produce great forces over a short travel with the hydraulic ram, but this was of little use in a crane. The use of racks and pinions to rotate winding drums had been tried with modest success, but the new method had all the benefits of simplicity. It worked like a block and tackle in reverse, with the ram and cylinder between the two blocks. When the water was turned on, the ram forced the two blocks apart, with

ABOVE: *Liverpool was the first port to use hydraulic power on a large scale. The man responsible for this was the Dock Engineer, Jesse Hartley, and in this view from the 1850s his characteristic granite buildings are prominent. The tallest of them is an accumulator house.*

BELOW, LEFT: *A representational diagram of a hydraulic accumulator. The ram, A, stands in cylinder B, the water being contained by the seals, C. Attached to the top of the ram is the yoke (D) which supports the weight bin (shown in outline). Filled with heavy waste material, this acts on the ram, creating an artificial head of water and thus controlled hydraulic power. As the ram is forced down, a control chain, attached to the weight bin, slackened and restarted pumps in order to maintain the head of water.*

BELOW, RIGHT: *A representational diagram of a jigger, a device used to magnify the stroke of a piston and used for lifts, cranes and other machines with long travels. The pulley system attached to the ram increases the length of chain or wire paid out relative to its own travel.*

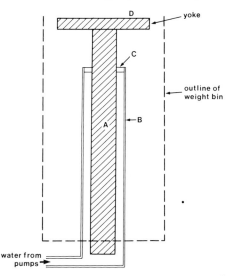

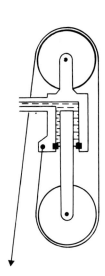

ABOVE, LEFT: *This view of an accumulator (from below) shows the cylinder, ram and control chain. When pressure in the system rises so does the ram, until the control chain stops the pumps. When power is drawn the pressure falls; so does the ram and the control chain restarts the pumps.*

ABOVE, RIGHT: *An accumulator viewed from above. The heavy yoke supports the ballast bin. This modest example (at Douglas Harbour, Isle of Man) has a bin 8 feet 4 inches (3.53 m) in diameter, 17 feet 5 inches (5.28 m) deep and weighing about 70 tons. The vertical travel is 17 feet (5.1 m).*

BELOW: *Hydraulic pumping stations were often of imposing appearance. This one, with its 'campanile', was even more imposing before it lost its top. Built in 1863 in Birkenhead, it powered a large system and is still in use.*

ABOVE: *This unmounted lock gate gives an impression of the quantity of wood and metal moved with apparent ease by dock gate engines.*

BELOW, LEFT: *Gates are normally still moved by hydraulic power: adjacent to most is an oily pit containing a ram and multiplying sheave. In a few cases, such as this at Alfred Entrance, Birkenhead, the lock-side is built up and the engines are accessible to the sightseer.*

BELOW, RIGHT: *The means of driving this capstan is not immediately apparent, a good reason for assuming that it is hydraulic powered. Capstans such as this were used in large numbers in ports and railway yards and allowed two men to move a ship or a train of railway wagons.*

the result that the free end of the chain or rope moved through a distance equal to the travel of the ram multiplied by the number of runs in motion in the 'tackle'. Since nature gives nothing away, the force available was divided by the same figure and diminished by the amount of friction in the system, which would vary between about eighteen and thirty per cent, depending on the multiplication ratio of the sheaves. The adoption of this device was probably responsible for the reputation which hydraulic machines gained for being rugged, reliable and easy to maintain. In numerical terms the machines which utilised the multiplying sheave dominated the industry, accounting for the vast majority of cranes, hoists, goods and passenger lifts and dock gate engines.

While Pascal and Bramah laid the basis of a distribution system without achieving it, Armstrong was an achiever: after his prototype crane of 1846, he sold two lifts and two cranes to Liverpool Docks in 1847-8 and by 1852 had completed another 146 cranes. His introduction of the accumulator in 1851 made his products more attractive and by 1858 he had sold twelve hundred machines, together with about three thousand installed horsepower and pumping plants. The principal customers were port authorities and railway companies.

Many important applications of hydraulics still remained in the future, but by the late 1850s Armstrong had turned theory and foresight into accepted engineering practice.

The Barton swing aqueduct carries the Bridgewater Canal over the Manchester Ship Canal. Unique in Britain, it shares a hydraulic pumping plant with the adjacent Barton road bridge. Here it is seen swinging back 'on' for Bridgewater traffic.

Every dock system of any size needs numerous movable bridges across its passages. Rolling lift bridges, like this one at Birkenhead East Float, were usually hydraulic, often driven by rotary motors. This one has been electrified, but retains its hydraulic machinery as a standby.

NEW APPLICATIONS FOR HYDRAULIC POWER

By the time that Armstrong had established extensive distribution systems in dock estates and railway goods yards, the young hydraulics industry had already made significant inroads into its two other major spheres of importance, the provision of mechanical power on great civil engineering projects and the driving of large single-purpose machines.

The railways had posed a number of new problems to civil engineers, one of which was a demand for bridges of unprecedented size across stretches of water. Among the earlier ones, Robert Stephenson's tubular girder bridges over the river Conwy and the Menai Straits were perhaps the most spectacular. The Menai bridge was the larger, using four great tubes, each 460 feet (140.2 m) long and weighing 1500 tons at a height of 90 feet (27.42 m) above high water level. When the work was completed and the bridge opened to traffic on 19th October 1851 there was great admiration of Stephenson and his colleagues, which has been perpetuated by historians, but designing a large span is only one part of the undertaking: placing it in position is equally important, and the great weight

of the Menai spans was silently raised inch by inch by hydraulic rams with a total capacity of 2620 tons. Not long before, the bridge could not have been built, nor could Brunel's Royal Albert Bridge at Saltash or many others.

Seven of the sections of the Menai bridge had been built by Ditchburn and Mare of Millwall, whose yard was soon to pass into the hands of John Scott Russell and become the construction site for Brunel's great ship the *Great Eastern*, which was to remain the biggest ship built for nearly forty years. After construction problems had ruined Scott Russell and driven even the ebullient Brunel to despair, further difficulties occurred in launching the ship. Brunel and Froude had calculated that a slope of one in twelve on the slipways would suffice to slide her into the water. Because there was no precedent for launching a ship of such size they provided steam winches and two hydraulic rams to encourage her should she stick. She did stick, and the combined efforts of the gear provided moved her about 3 feet (1 m) towards the water. 23rd November 1857 was to have been a triumphal day when all the diffi-

13

culties were overcome but many weeks of humiliation and grinding toil passed before hydraulic rams with a total thrust of 4500 tons succeeded in coaxing the 12,000 ton ship into the Thames. One of the machines employed was a 20 inch (507 mm) veteran from the Menai bridge. Richard Tangye, who provided much of the hydraulic equipment, is said to have remarked that his firm had launched the *Great Eastern* and the *Great Eastern* had launched his firm.

The most spectacular of the single-purpose installations belong to the later part of the nineteenth century, but before the *Great Eastern* was launched a number of notable examples had been completed. The first hydraulic movable bridge of which we have a definite record was built by J. W. Rendell at Kingsbridge in Devon in 1831, though it was probably preceded by a small one over the Rochdale Canal in Manchester before 1825. Hydraulic power was admirably suited to the driving of movable bridges by virtue of its slow and gentle application of great force, and once the accumulator became available it had the further advantage of carrying a reserve of power to overcome initial sticking of the span. An accumulator with a ram of 12 inches (305 mm) diameter and a stroke of 20 feet (6.09 m) is not unusually large, but at a pressure of 700 pounds per square inch (49.2 kg/sq cm) it would provide a reserve, above and beyond the power of the engine, of 48 horsepower for one minute to gain the initial momentum. As ports grew in size and complexity, and as railway companies sought ever more crossings of navigable waterways, the demand for movable bridges was bound to increase. By 1869 Armstrong alone had supplied more than fifty, though some of these did not have their own pumps, being connected to existing mains systems.

The increasing quantities of coal being burned by ships, engine houses, furnaces and railway locomotives produced a demand for better methods of handling coal. The cost of moving general cargo in ports had been cut by up to 87.5 per cent by the adoption of hydraulic hoists, and those whose business it was to move coal looked for similar savings. In some cases the machinery chosen was modest, but in others spectacular machines for handling loads of tens of tons at a time were devised, of which the 'Tom Pudding tippers' at Goole are probably the best surviving example. In ironworks and gasworks hydraulic handling systems for the raw materials, the product and the waste began to appear. The widespread introduction of steel and the adoption of armour on warships speeded the process. As tougher and stronger materials began to be used, greater power was needed in the tools to work them and that power was often hydraulic.

Ralph Tweddell had invented a hydraulic boiler tube expander, but his hydraulic riveter, patented in 1866, was to have much further reaching effects. Although iron ships and iron bridges had been built long before then, it suddenly became possible to close rivets much better and much faster than ever before. The costs of some of the great structures of the last quarter of the nineteenth century would otherwise have been so much greater that many of them would probably never have been built.

Bramah's patent of 1812 had envisaged power distribution not only within industrial estates but also as a supply to the public. It was a long time before that idea was taken up, but in 1876 the first public supply company began pumping, in Hull. It was only a small undertaking, with the 'spine' of its system of mains less than a mile long, but it paved the way for other and larger systems. By far the largest was in London, with a maximum extent of 186 miles (299.2 km), but substantial systems were also constructed in Liverpool, Manchester, Glasgow and Birmingham. In the same way that Armstrong had succeeded in dominating the market for dockside equipment, so public supply networks, in Britain and other countries, were influenced by a single man, E. B. Ellington. Consultant to the Hull Hydraulic Power Company for the establishment of their system, he was also managing director of the Hydraulic Engineering Company of Chester, which was the leading supplier of equipment to the public systems. The ethics of such an arrangement would now be frowned upon, but Ellington acted on both sides of the deal in the construction of the

ABOVE: *Top and bottom views of a simple three cylinder capstan. Made by the Hydraulic Engineering Company, it is typical of machines found in large numbers in ports and railway goods yards.*

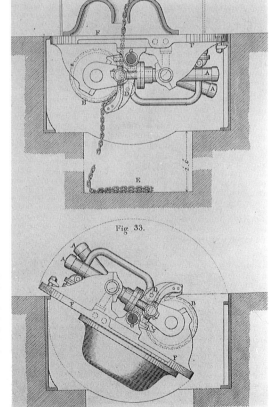

Fig 33.

RIGHT: *A much less common device was this 'hauling machine' installed at Cardiff Docks in 1874. The pivot (G) is not only a mounting, but carries the supply water at one end and the exhaust water at the other. The whole machine could thus be rolled over (as in the lower diagram) for maintenance purposes without the need to disconnect the hydraulic system.*

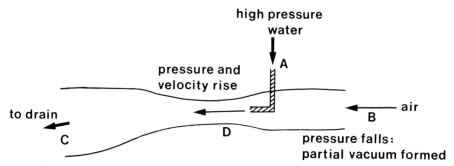

The hydraulic ejector, used in Ellington's fire extinguisher, the hydraulic vacuum cleaner and other such machines. High pressure water is introduced at inlet A, ejecting to a drain at C. The constriction at D raises the pressure and velocity, creating a partial vacuum at B. Air and waste are sucked in, mixed with water and evacuated to the drain.

systems mentioned above.

The public systems offered to smaller industrial concerns all the benefits of the private networks set up by large enterprises, and as a result they found a ready demand and early prosperity. The London system started pumping in 1883 from a pumphouse in Blackfriars, and by 1895 had 76 miles (122 km) of mains in use delivering 9.5 million gallons (43.1 million litres) per week. The peak was in 1927 when 31.7 million gallons (144 million litres) were pumped, providing a supply to eight thousand machines. Because these public supply companies became so large, they were able to offer economies of scale which tempted some private systems to give up pumping for themselves and buy power instead.

Ellington was more than a shrewd salesman: he was also a considerable innovator, and in particular he was associated with a reappraisal of hydrokinetic machines. The most numerous machines used by the public supply customers were, and remained, simple ram-driven devices, mainly lifts, hoists and presses, but a number of machines were introduced which depended on passing high-pressure water through a nozzle in a *venturi*. Perhaps the best known of these was Ellington's patent fire extinguisher. This mixed high-pressure water with a town mains supply: the result was not only a higher pressure at the nozzle, but a positive suction to increase the rate of delivery from the main. At the top of a high building in a drought this could be very useful. It gave the benefits of a steam fire pump at a fraction of the cost, though we may be sceptical about one of the benefits claimed. It could be used, it was said, with only high-pressure water on, to break down doors as a means of escape. An understanding of the third law of motion (that to every action there is an equal and opposite reaction) will reveal that the operator strong enough to hold back the reaction at the jet during this operation is also by definition strong enough to break down the door with his bare hands.

The use of the partial vacuum generated in a venturi was extended to ejector pumps for the transfer of fluids in works, but perhaps its most engaging application was the hydraulic vacuum cleaner, which was quite widely used for a time in offices, hotels and public buildings. A central ejector, usually in a cellar, evacuated a system of pipes concealed in the skirting boards, to any one of which a cleaning head much like that of a modern cylinder vacuum cleaner could be attached. Advertising material for these made great play of the fact that the dust went down the drain with the exhaust water, in silence, and the electric rival was attacked in dismissive manner: 'an electric vacuum cleaner does not remove dust; it merely filters it.'

By the 1890s electric power distribu-

16

ABOVE: *The need for a railway bridge to cross a channel which had to be used by shipping often led to the construction of a movable bridge. The Hawarden Bridge, carrying the Wrexham-Bidston line across the river Dee, had a movable span 285 feet (86.6 m) long, which weighed 700 tons. It was hydraulically operated, but has now been fixed in place.*

BELOW: *The operating cylinders of the Hawarden Bridge are plainly visible below the huge pivot. Power came from a small pumphouse (now demolished) on the Wirral side. The hydraulic equipment was connected with the railway signals, which had to be at 'danger' before the bridge could be opened.*

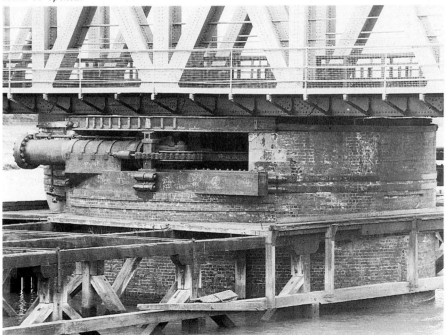

RIGHT: *Steelworking machinery demanded a considerable amount of force and was therefore a fruitful market for the hydraulic engineer. In 1888 Henry Berry of Leeds supplied a number of machines such as these billet shears to the Aireside Steel and Iron Company.*

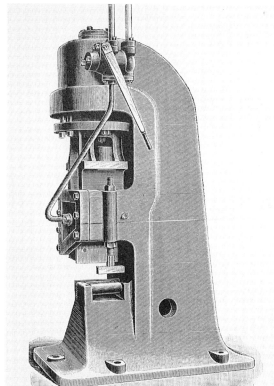

BELOW: *Steel is also heavy and steelworks used hydraulic machinery for handling as well as working their materials and products. This machine, with a hydraulic ram on the left, was part of an ingot transit system which moved large pieces of steel from one process to the next.*

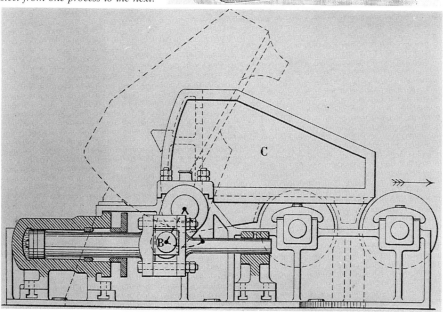

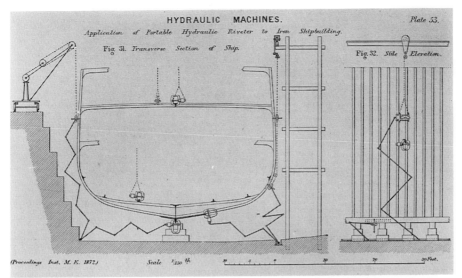

Application of Portable Hydraulic Riveter to Iron Shipbuilding.

Fig. 31. *Transverse Section of Ship.*

Fig. 32. *Side Elevation.*

(Proceedings Inst. M. E. 1872.)   Scale ¹⁄₁₅₀ᵗʰ

ABOVE: *The hydraulic riveter not only produced better quality work than hand riveting, but it was quicker, cheaper and silent. This diagram shows some of the ways it was applied in shipbuilding, and also illustrates the system of universal joints used in the supply piping.*

BELOW: *Few heavy industries did not employ hydraulic power at some time. This photograph shows a hydraulic charging machine serving a bank of retorts in a typical gasworks of the 1890s.*

tion was becoming a serious rival, but Ellington was not a man to give up easily, nor was aggressive advertising his only resort. While voltages remained low, transmission losses were high and there was, briefly, a market for hydraulically driven generators, mainly for lighting. To attain the necessary speed, these were normally hydrokinetic, usually driven by a Pelton wheel. (The Pelton wheel is a small, highly efficient waterwheel in which a jet of water impinges on the inside of a cup on the end of each spoke in turn. The complete reversal of water flow which results is the key to its efficiency, and this can be experienced by

rudimentary experiment with a hemispherical soup ladle under the kitchen tap.)

Ellington's greatest success in this brief period of counter-attack was the establishment in 1893 of the electric lighting system in Antwerp, where small generating stations housed generators driven by hydraulic turbine motors.

By 1900 hydraulic power could be applied to almost any purpose for which power might be required, and in almost any location. Only the rapid improvement of its one serious rival, electric power distribution, could prevent its continued progress.

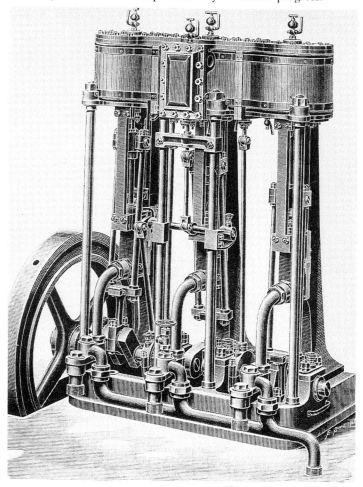

A small vertical steam hydraulic pumping set, built to the design of E. B. Ellington by the Hydraulic Engineering Company. It delivered about 9 gallons (40.8 litres) per minute at 700 pounds per square inch (49.2 kg/sq cm) which represents about 18 horsepower output.

Tower Bridge is one of the most prominent hydraulic machines in the world, though many people fail to realise this. To those who do not commute across it, it is a matter of regret that it is seldom raised nowadays.

THE GOLDEN AGE OF HYDRAULIC MACHINES

The years between the Franco-Prussian War and the First World War were the golden age of the huge machine and the mighty structure. As would be expected from the developments in hydraulic power already described, hydraulic machines were at the forefront of the engineers' campaign to extend the limits of their technology.

Access from the Mersey to the Cheshire saltfields had long been the basis of an important heavy chemicals industry, whose demand was well served by the Weaver Navigation. Beyond its reach were further salt deposits served by the Trent and Mersey Canal, and it was to improve access to the latter that the Anderton Boat Lift was opened in 1876. Like many other hydraulic machines, its approach to the problem was simplistic. If you wish to raise a boat 50 feet (15 m), you float it into a tank of water, shut the gate and lift tank and boat together. The lift, built by Leader Williams, is still one of the wonders of the waterways system, but unfortunately its hydraulic system was damaged by frost in 1908 and it was

electrified, with radical alterations to its appearance.

Hydraulics were used at sea as well. The coaling pontoon *Atlas* of 1858 is perhaps a special case, but by the 1870s steamers with hydraulic steering motors were appearing, together with hydraulic reversing gear, winches, ash-handling hoists and capstans. The armoured warship not only required hydraulic power to build it but, after HMS *Temeraire*, included an impressive array of hydraulic machines aboard. Her gun turrets were trained hydraulically, and the complicated procedure required to load the short muzzle-loading big guns still favoured by the Admiralty was hydraulically powered, as were the ammunition hoists. In 1886 HMS *Colossus* was armed with the hydraulically trained and loaded breech-loading big gun in substantially the form which would last out the age of the battleship. The worldwide power of the late Victorian navy was based not only on coal and iron, but on high-pressure water as well. In 1886 the supreme monument to hydraulic

RIGHT: *When the movable gun turret was first adopted on warships various methods of training the guns were tried. The small and accurate adjustments of position of these very heavy structures became and remained a hydraulic function. This is the training gear of X turret on HMS 'Belfast'.*

BELOW: *Dreadnoughts and 'Atlantic Greyhounds' alike needed a servo mechanism to move their immense rudders. By their standards the tiller flat of HMS 'Belfast' is small, but the rams in the background, which provide the necessary power, are nonetheless substantial pieces of machinery.*

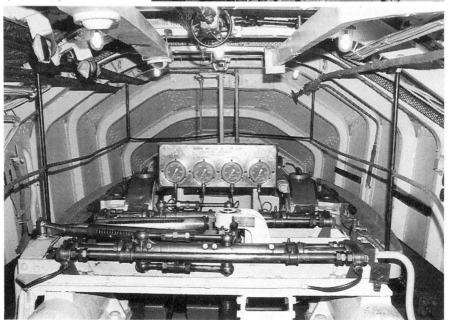

The Forth Railway Bridge is a fitting monument to a school of engineering which scorned problems of size and weight. The power which dug, lifted, sheared, shaped, punched and riveted this magnificent structure was hydraulic.

machines as a building service, the Forth Bridge, was still under construction. 55,000 tons of steel plates were formed into shape with hydraulic presses and joined together with six million rivets, mostly closed with hydraulic machines. Twenty-three stationary pumps provided water at pressures up to 3920 pounds per square inch (275.5 kg/sq cm) to operate not only riveters but cranes, lifting rams and Sir William Arroll's celebrated hydraulic spade. When the Prince of Wales opened the Forth Bridge on 4th March 1890 he appropriately did so by closing the last rivet — hydraulically.

Before the Forth Bridge was built, the Channel Tunnel had been exercising the minds of the hydraulic engineers, and there was a proposal in 1882 for an automatic tunnelling machine, which would bore its way through the chalk stratum, reducing the spoil to a slurry with its own exhaust water and pumping it back from the working face.

Unlimited force at the end of a pipe was an invaluable aid for any engineer working on one of the epic projects of the late nineteenth century. A ship lift at Halifax, Nova Scotia, with a capacity of 2000 tons and a forging press at Sheffield with a power of 4000 tons involved no innovation, just size and brute force. A movable bridge was required over the Thames at London to reconcile the problems of crossing and navigation with the prohibitive cost of land for approaches to a high-level bridge. The moving parts weighed 3000 tons. The technology existed and it provided us with Tower Bridge, a magnificent monument which functions hydraulically to this day.

Hydraulic machines spread around the world. When the French navy sought to re-equip its dockyard at Toulon, they engaged Ralph Tweddell as consultant, and an impressive array of hydraulic equipment was installed. Ellington equipped a public supply company in Mel-

Hydraulic engineers invariably made their structures as impressive as possible. This pumping station, at Bramley-Moore Dock, Liverpool, provided power for mundane coaling jobs but shows considerable attention to architectural detail.

bourne and also solved the sewage problem in Buenos Aires with an ingenious system of small hydraulically driven pumps in sumps at various points about the system driven from a central pumping station.

Some of its applications were of a lighter nature. Where there was a public supply it was the invariable choice for theatre safety curtains, for not only would it continue to function in the event of a fire, but it could not start one and it could help extinguish one. The revolving stage and the Demon King's entrance on the trap, and later the Wurlitzer organ rising through the stage already playing, all were achieved by hydraulic power. Its

safety was reflected in substantial insurance discounts offered to theatres which were thus equipped.

If hydraulic machines could be said metaphorically to underlie many great engineering achievements, the Eiffel Tower is one which they underlay physically. It was intended as a structural masterpiece, a display of prowess for its own sake. With its hydraulic lifts and its hydraulic levelling gear it depended as much on the work of the hydraulic engineer as did many other less self-conscious structures. The visitor appeal of a 1000 foot (300 m) tower which could be ascended only on foot would have been very limited.

ABOVE: *The steam pumping engines of Tower Bridge when they were still in operation. The decline in shipping entering the Pool of London led to their being replaced with a power supply from the London Hydraulic Power Company. In 1976 a self-contained electric pumping system, operating oil rather than water hydraulics, was installed.*

BELOW: *The Manchester Ship Canal remains a major user of hydraulic machinery. Old Quay swing bridge is typical of a movable bridge, with its pumphouse, accumulator tower and control cabin alongside. The proposed closure of the canal above Runcorn would leave Eastham Locks as the only site where hydraulics still function.*

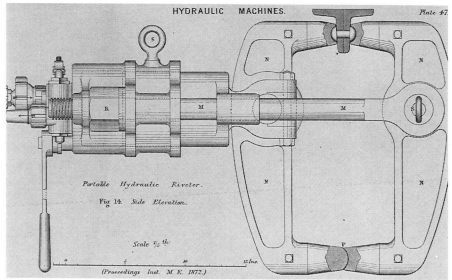

Portable Hydraulic Riveter.

Fig. 14. Side Elevation.

Scale 1/5 th

(Proceedings Inst. M. E. 1872.)

ABOVE: *A sectional diagram of a typical hydraulic riveter, pioneered by Ralph Tweddell, which made possible great improvements in productivity in the building of large riveted structures.*

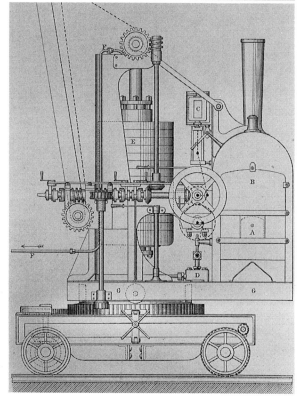

RIGHT: *The hydraulic riveter was rapidly accepted in shipyards, but many engineering projects did not have a convenient power supply nearby. Tweddell therefore invented this rail-mounted riveting plant, incorporating boiler, engine, pump, accumulator, riveter and small crane for positioning the riveter.*

ABOVE: *The Anderton boat lift was a hydraulic balance on a large scale: the caissons sat on rams in cylinders which were in hydraulic communication. Very little overhead structure was needed compared with the forest of columns added when it was converted to electricity and power input was only required to make good the effects of leakage.*

LEFT: *Impressive though the Anderton lift was, it was dwarfed by this machine at La Louviere in Belgium, which had rams 6 feet 6¾ inches (1.99 m) diameter and 63 feet 11 inches (19.4 m) long. The caissons were 141 feet 7 inches (42.9 m) long by 18 feet 5 inches (5.5 m) wide compared with Anderton's 70 feet (21.2 m) by 14 feet (4.25 m).*

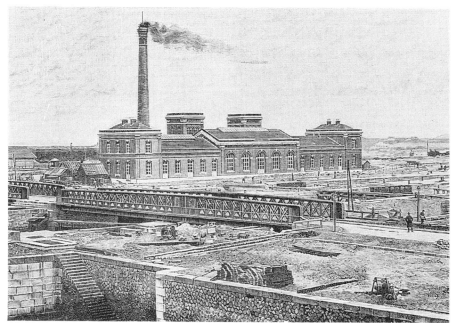

ABOVE: *The new harbour works at Calais, completed in 1899, included hydraulic machinery for gates, sluices, bridges and capstans. This elegant building contained the two 50 horsepower steam engines and their pumps together with boiler house and accumulators. The whole installation was of French design and was built by the Fives-Lille Company.*

LEFT: *Where hydraulic power was used to drive small rotating machinery a common choice was the simple and reliable Brotherhood motor. This example drove a sand-washing machine at a water authority filterbed.*

ABOVE: *Even astronomers depended on hydraulics. The Lick Observatory, California, not only rotated its dome hydraulically, but also moved its observation floor up and down through a travel of 16 feet 6 inches (5 m) to follow the eyepiece as it trained in the vertical plane.*

RIGHT: *When Gustave Eiffel designed what was then the tallest structure in the world he seems to have lacked faith in his construction team. The columns of the Eiffel Tower rested on great hydraulic rams which could be used to set it square should it be built crooked.*

The growth of electric power stations changed the economics of engineering, making it cheaper to produce hydraulic power electrically with machines such as this 1924 Hathorn Davey triplex pump, used by the Liverpool Hydraulic Power Company.

THE DECLINE OF HYDRAULIC MACHINES

The rapid rise in the early years of the twentieth century of electrical power transmission could not fail to damage public hydraulic systems, especially in the lighter applications and in those requiring high-speed rotative motion. On the other hand, the superiority of hydraulic power for slow-moving machines where great force was required was so great that further explanations of decline must be found. One is that, as electricity generating stations became first large and then huge, economies of scale meant that the comparatively tiny hydraulic pumping stations could not compete. Those which were still in use after the Second World War had mostly, in a reversal of the economics of Antwerp, converted their steam-driven pumps to electric driving.

There were physical failings as well. Most of the mains were made of iron, and progressive corrosion over the decades increased friction losses, reduced cross-sectional areas and released particles of scale, which scored glands and seals causing leakage and hence power loss. In the last weeks of operation of one system there was a standing loss — a wastage of power when no machine was drawing water — of nearly 60 per cent. One large Plurivane pump was running almost constantly just to keep the accumulators up. In all systems the detection of underground leaks was difficult until they became serious, and the procedure of cleaning the mains periodically was neglected because of financial stringency, causing the problem to get progressively worse.

Hydraulic systems suffered heavily during the Second World War. Their mains tended to be concentrated in areas which were priority targets for the Luftwaffe, in docks, railway yards and heavy industrial complexes in major cities. Cast iron mains with numerous joints were easily damaged by bombing.

The public systems suffered equally

heavily in the aftermath of the war, with wholesale relocation of industries in suburban and even rural areas. The hydraulic supply companies could not follow their customers and were left to offer their services to the inner city deserts thus created. Private systems suffered in similar ways, but more particularly from the shift in emphasis to lighter industries, from the changes in freight handling brought about by container traffic and from the tendency of ports to creep closer to the sea to accommodate larger ships and cut dredging costs. In each case the hydraulic systems tended to become obsolete.

Hydraulic machines have not disappeared altogether, though they are now scarce. Within a few industrial enclaves and parts of some dock areas Armstrong-style systems still function. Distribution is almost dead, but there is still a requirement for hydraulic power. Huge metal extrusion presses, tobacco presses and dock gate engines are still relatively common. The Harbour Bridge at Douglas, Isle of Man, is a new bridge on top of old working gear, and other movable bridges still function in the old manner. The difference is one of principle: these single-purpose installations are not distribution systems; they are machines for the multiplication of forces.

ABOVE: *A small hydraulic pump with belt drive, originally for an oil engine but now electrically driven. It operates the Douglas Harbour bridge, Isle of Man.*

BELOW: *When tobacco is blended, different leaves are required to mingle the juices and flavours. By the beginning of the twentieth century the usual method of achieving this was by hydraulic presses such as this one in Liverpool, where it is still in service.*

FURTHER READING

McNeil, I. *Hydraulic Power*. Longman, 1972.
Pugh, B. *The Hydraulic Age*. Mechanical Engineering Press, 1980.

These are the only modern books on the subject, and the reader who seeks more must go back to the sources, of which the Proceedings of the Institution of Mechanical Engineers, the Minutes of the Proceedings of the Institute of Civil Engineers and the journals *The Engineer* and *Engineering* are the most fruitful. Nineteenth-century volumes of these are found only in major libraries but are worth the effort. In each case indexing is efficient and browsing productive.

For light relief, 'The Engineer's Thumb', from *The Adventures of Sherlock Holmes* by Sir Arthur Conan Doyle, gives a fictional sidelight.

PLACES TO VISIT

Intending visitors are advised to find out the times of opening before making a special journey.

Birmingham Museum of Science and Industry, Newhall Street, Birmingham B3 1RZ. Telephone: 021-236 1022.

The Boat Museum, Dockyard Road, Ellesmere Port, Cheshire L65 4EF. Telephone: 051-355 5017. (Working Armstrong steam pump, and other equipment.)

Bradford Industrial Museum, Moorside Road, Eccleshill, Bradford, West Yorkshire BD2 3HP. Telephone: Bradford (0274) 631756.

Leeds Industrial Museum, Armley Mill, Canal Road, Armley, Leeds, West Yorkshire. Telephone: Leeds (0532) 637862.

Merseyside County Museums, William Brown Street, Liverpool, Merseyside L3 8EN. Telephone: 051-207 0001 or 5451.

Museum of Science and Engineering, Blandford House, West Blandford Street, Newcastle upon Tyne, Tyne and Wear. Telephone: Newcastle upon Tyne (0632) 326789. (The largest collection of hydraulic machines; some splendid items.)

Royal Scottish Museum, Chambers Street, Edinburgh EH1 1JF. Telephone: 031-225 7534.

Science Museum, Exhibition Road, South Kensington, London SW7 2DD. Telephone: 01-589 3456. (A substantial collection.)

Thames Barrier Centre, 1 Unity Way, Woolwich, London SE18 5NJ. Telephone: 01-854 1373. (The Centre includes displays on the working of the Barrier.)

Tower Bridge, London E1. Telephone: 01-407 0922. (The towers, walkways and engine rooms are open to the public.)

In addition, many places not open to visitors have working hydraulic machinery which is accessible in varying degrees. The famous Newcastle Swing Bridge, although electrically pumped, is a good example, as are many of the machines mentioned in the text. In some cases it is necessary to seek the owner's permission to visit.